The Complete Guitar Player Paul Simon Songbook

by Arthur Dick.

Wise Publications
London/New York/Sydney/Cologne

Exclusive distributors:
Music Sales Limited
8/9 Frith Street, London W1V 5TZ, England.
Music Sales Pty Limited
120, Rothschild Avenue, Rosebery, NSW 2018, Australia

This book © Copyright 1988 by Wise Publications
ISBN 0.7119.1156.8 Order No. PS10875

Art direction by Mike Bell.
Cover photography by Peter Wood.
Styling by Penny Legg.
Arranged and compiled by Arthur Dick.
Typesetting by Capital Setters.

Music Sales complete catalogue lists thousands of titles and is free from
your local music shop, or direct from Music Sales Limited. Please send
£1.75 (cheque) for postage to Music Sales Limited, 8/9 Frith Street,
London W1V 5TZ, England.

Printed in England by
St Edmundsbury Press Limited, Bury St Edmunds, Suffolk.

I Am A Rock Paul Simon

4/4 Rhythm/Strumming/Lively
See Course Book No. 1 Page 12

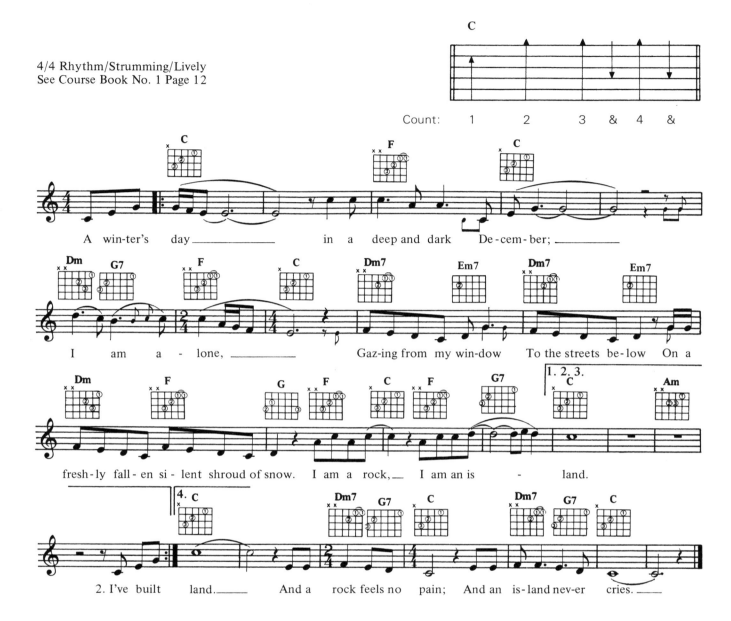

Verse 2
(I've built) — walls,
A fortress deep and mighty
That none may penetrate,
I have no need of friendship
Friendship causes pain,
Its laughter and loving I disdain.

Verse 3
Don't talk of love,
But I've heard the word before;
It's sleeping in my memory
I won't disturb the slumber of feelings that have died
If I never loved I never would have cried.

Verse 4
I have my books,
And my poetry to protect me.
I am shielded in my armour,
Hiding in my room, safe within my womb,
I touch no one and no one touches me.

Blessed   Paul Simon

3/4 Rhythm Strumming
See Course Book No. 1 Page 9

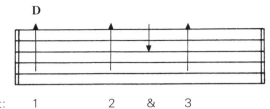

Count: 1   2   &   3

Bless-ed are the meek for they shall in-her-it.

Bless-ed is the lamb whose blood flows.____

____   Bless-ed are the sat up-on,____

Spat up-on,____ Rat - ted on._____   O

Lord,____   Why have you for-sa-ken me?

I got no place to go,_____ I've walked a-round So-ho for the last

night or so   Ah, but it does-n't mat-ter,____ no.____

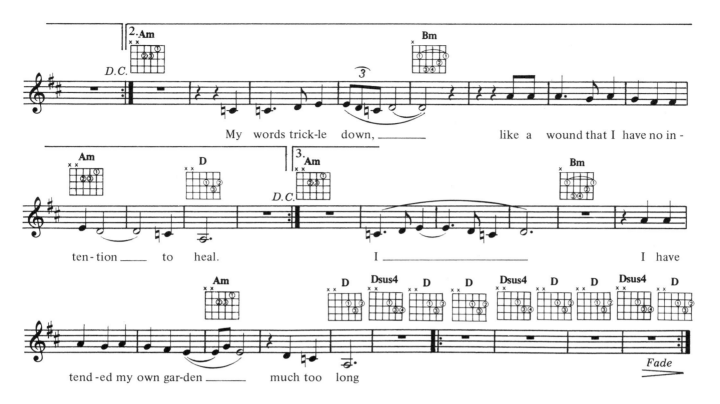

My words trick-le down, _____ like a wound that I have no in-ten-tion _____ to heal. I _____ I have tend-ed my own gar-den _____ much too long

Fade

Verse 2
Blessed is the land and the kingdom.
Blessed is the man whose soul belongs to
Blessed are the meth drinkers, pot seelers, illusion dwellers
O - Lord, why have you forsaken me?
My words trickle down.
Like a wound I have no intention to heal.

Verse 3
Blessed are the stained glass, window pane glass
Blessed is the church service makes me nervous,
Blessed are the penny rookers, cheap hookers, groovy lookers
O - Lord, why have you forsaken me?
I have tended my garden much too long.

The Only Living Boy In New York Paul Simon

4/4 Rhythm Strumming
See Course Book No. 1 Page 12

Count: 1   2   3 & 4 &

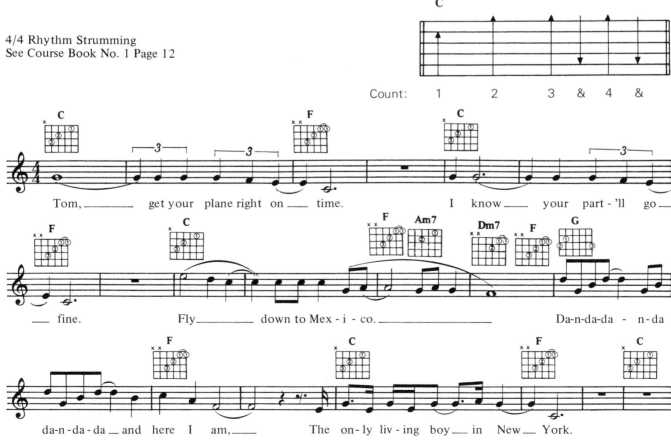

Tom, _____ get your plane right on _____ time. I know _____ your part -'ll go _____ fine. Fly _____ down to Mex - i - co. _____ Da-n-da-da - n-da da-n-da-da _____ and here I am, _____ The on-ly liv-ing boy _____ in New _____ York.

Papa Hobo
Paul Simon

3/4 Rhythm/Strumming
See Course Book No. 1 Page 14

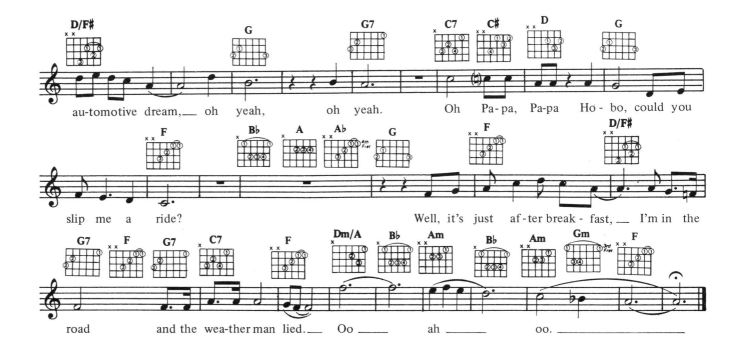

au-tomotive dream,__ oh yeah, oh yeah. Oh Pa-pa, Pa-pa Ho-bo, could you slip me a ride? Well, it's just af-ter break-fast, __ I'm in the road and the wea-ther man lied.__ Oo __ ah __ oo. _____

Richard Cory   Paul Simon

4/4 Rhythm/Bass-Strum
See Course Book No. 1 Pages 15 and 22

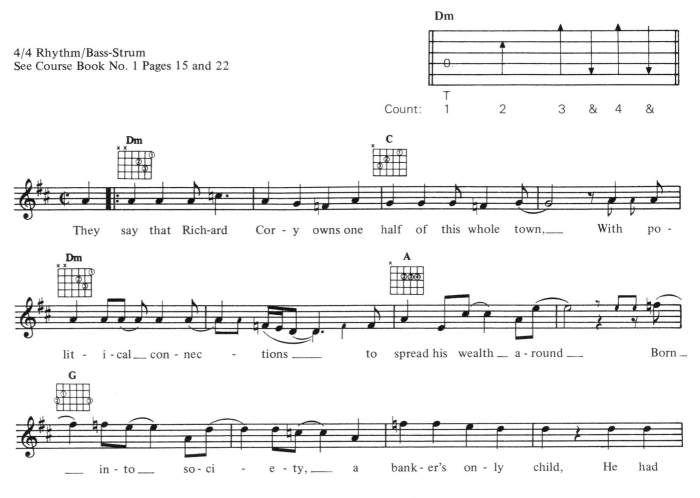

They say that Rich-ard Cor-y owns one half of this whole town,__ With po-lit-i-cal __ con-nec - tions ____ to spread his wealth __ a-round __ Born __ __ in-to __ so-ci - e-ty, __ a bank-er's on-ly child, He had

8

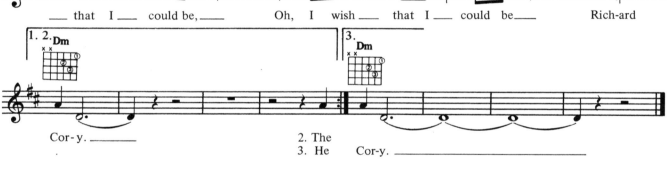

Verse 2
The papers print his picture almost everywhere he goes
Richard Cory at the opera, Richard Cory at a show.
And the rumour of his parties and the orgies on his yacht!
Oh, the survey must be happy with everything he's got.

Verse 3
He freely gave to charity, he had the common touch,
And they were grateful for his patronage, and they thanked him very much,
So my mind was filled with wonder when the evening headlines read:
"Richard Cory went home last night and put a bullet through his head."

Cecilia   Paul Simon

4/4 Rhythm/Strumming
See Course Book No. 1 Page 14

ing. ___ Ju- bi ing. ___ Oh oh ___ oh oh oh oh oh oh oh ___ oh

oh oh oh oh ___ oh oh oh ___ oh. ___ Oh oh ___ oh. ___ Come on home. ___

Hey Schoolgirl Paul Simon & Art Garfunkel

4/4 Rhythm/Bass-Strum
See Course Book No. 1 Page 15

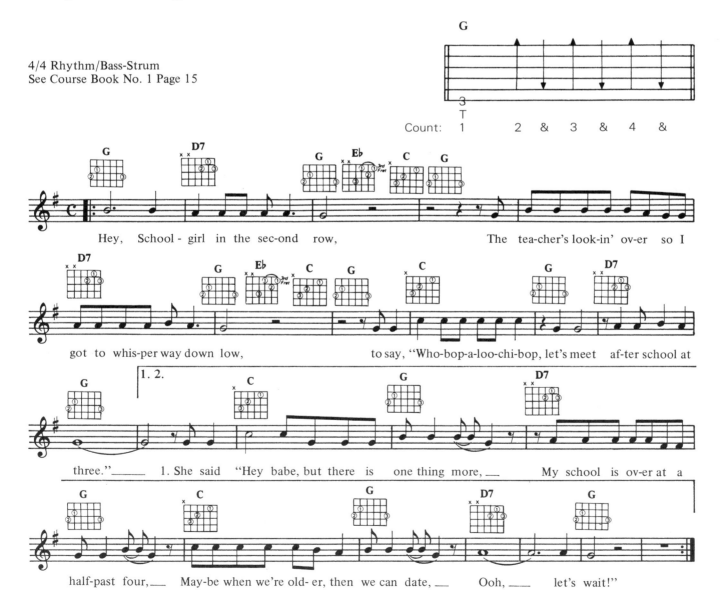

Hey, School-girl in the sec-ond row, The tea-cher's look-in' ov-er so I

got to whis-per way down low, to say, "Who-bop-a-loo-chi-bop, let's meet af-ter school at

three." ___ 1. She said "Hey babe, but there is one thing more, ___ My school is ov-er at a

half-past four, ___ May-be when we're old-er, then we can date, ___ Ooh, ___ let's wait!"

11

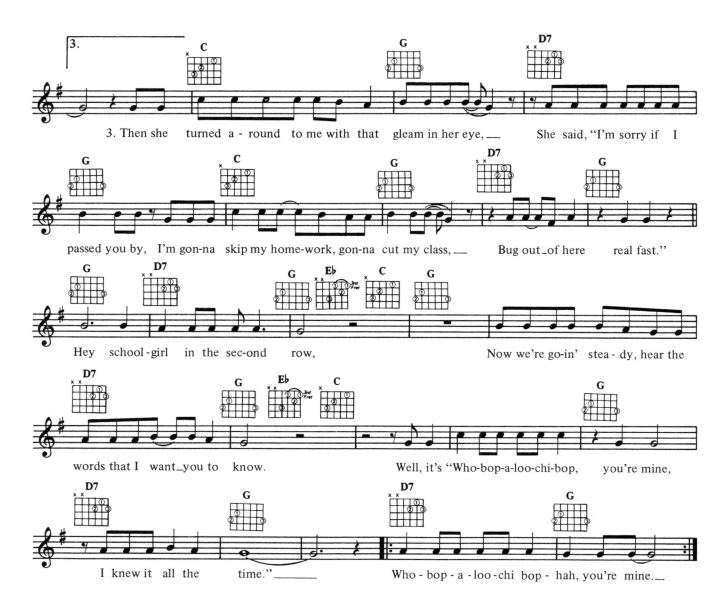

3. Then she turned a - round to me with that gleam in her eye, __ She said, "I'm sorry if I

passed you by, I'm gon-na skip my home-work, gon-na cut my class, __ Bug out _ of here real fast."

Hey school - girl in the sec-ond row, Now we're go-in' stea - dy, hear the

words that I want _ you to know. Well, it's "Who-bop-a-loo-chi-bop, you're mine,

I knew it all the time." _____ Who - bop - a - loo -chi bop - hah, you're mine. __

Verse 2
She said "Hey, babe, I gotta lot to do,
It takes me hours till my homework's thru,
Someday we'll go steady, so don't you fret,
Ooh, not yet!"

Silent Eyes Paul Simon

3/4 Rhythm/Bass-Strum
See Course Book No. 1 Page 17

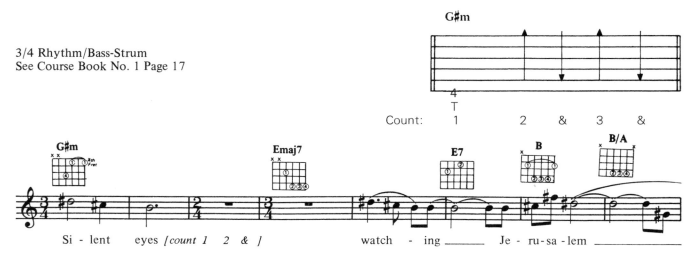

Si - lent eyes *[count 1 2 &]* watch - ing _____ Je - ru - sa - lem

make her bed ___ of stones.

Si - lent eyes. no one will com - fort her; ___ Je - ru - sa - lem ___

___ weeps a - lone. She is sor - row,

sor - row; she burns like a flame ___ and she calls ___

___ my name. ___ Si - lent eyes

burn - ing in the des - ert sun ___ half-way to Je - ru - sa - lem.

And we shall all be called ___ as wit-ness-es, each and ev -'ry - one, to stand ___ be - fore ___ the

eyes ___ of God and speak what was ___ done. ___

7 O'Clock News/Silent Night Paul Simon & Art Garfunkel

3/4 Rhythm/Bass-Strum Lightly
See Course Book No. 1 Page 22

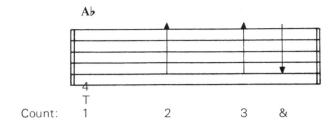

Count: 1   2   3   &

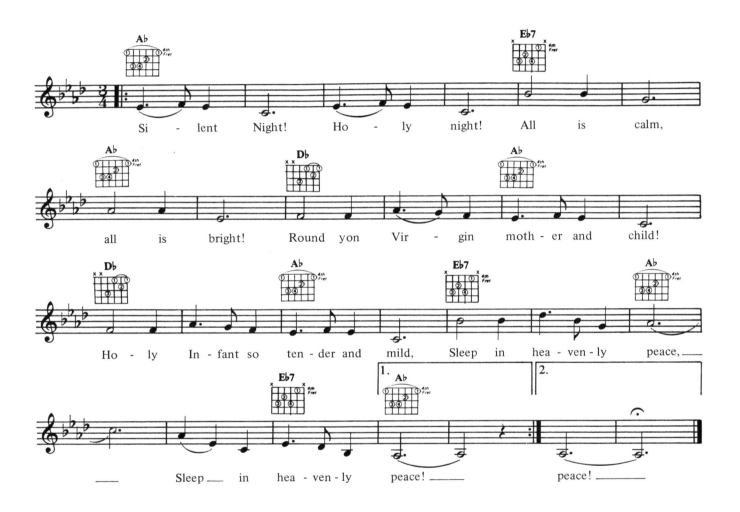

Si - lent Night! Ho - ly night! All is calm,

all is bright! Round yon Vir - gin moth - er and child!

Ho - ly In - fant so ten - der and mild, Sleep in hea - ven - ly peace, ___

___ Sleep ___ in hea - ven - ly peace! ___ peace! ___

Song For The Asking Paul Simon

Hammer/Bass-Strum
See Course Book No. 2 Page 12

Here is my song for the ask-ing,___

Ask me and I will play so sweet-ly, I'll___ make you smile; This is my

tune for the tak-ing,___ Take it, don't turn a-way I've been wait-ing ___ all my___ life. ___

— Think-ing it ov-er, I've been sad, _____ Think-ing it ov-er, I'd be

more than glad to change my ways ___ for the ask-ing, Ask me and I ___ will

play All the love that I _____ hold in-side.

The Big Bright Green Pleasure Machine   Paul Simon

4/4 Rhythm/Strumming/Swing/lively
See Course Book No. 2 Page 8

1. Do peo - ple have a ten - den - cy to dump__ on you?__ Does
your group have more cav - i - ties__ than theirs?__ Do all the hip - pies seem__
__ to get the jump__ on you?__ Do you sleep__ a - lone when oth - ers sleep in pairs?
__ Well, there's no need to com - plain,__ We'll e - lim - i - nate your pain.__
__ We can neu - tral - ize__ your brain.__ You'll feel just __ fine __ now. __ Buy a
Big Bright __ Green _____ Plea - sure Ma - chine! 2. Do
chine! chine! You bet - ter hur - ry up and
or - der one. __ Our lim - it - ed __ sup - ply is ve - ry near - ly gone. Do you

16

Verse 2

Do figures of authority just shoot you down?
Is life within the bus'ness world a drag?
Did your boss just mention that you'd better shop around,
To find yourself a more productive bag?
Are you worried and distressed?
Can't seem to get no rest?
Put our product to the test.

You'll feel just fine now,
Buy a big bright green pleasure machine!

You better hurry up and order one,
Our limited supply is very nearly gone.

Verse 3

Do you nervously await the blows of cruel fate?
Do your checks bounce higher than a rubber ball?
Are you worried 'cause your girl friend's just a little late?

Are you looking for a way to chuck it all?
We can end your daily strife,
At a reasonable price,
You've seen it advertised in 'Life'.

You'll feel just fine now,
Buy a big bright green pleasure machine!

Kodachrome* Paul Simon

4/4 Rhythm/Strumming
See Course Book No. 2 Page 10

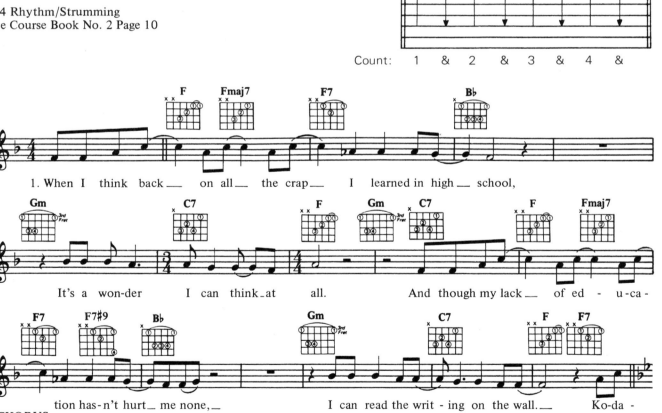

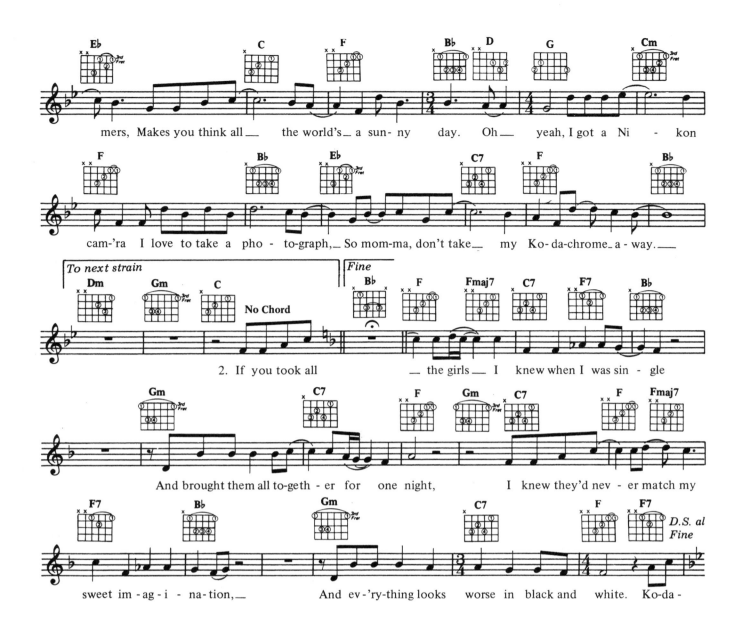

mers, Makes you think all — the world's a sun- ny day. Oh— yeah, I got a Ni - kon

cam-'ra I love to take a pho - to-graph,— So mom-ma, don't take— my Ko-da-chrome— a - way.—

To next strain / *Fine*

No Chord

2. If you took all — the girls — I knew when I was sin - gle

And brought them all to-geth - er for one night, I knew they'd nev - er match my

sweet im - ag - i - na-tion,— And ev -'ry-thing looks worse in black and white. Ko-da-

D.S. al Fine

Take Me To The Mardi Gras Paul Simon

4/4 Rhythm/Strumming/Stress 3rd upstroke
See Course Book No. 2 Page 10

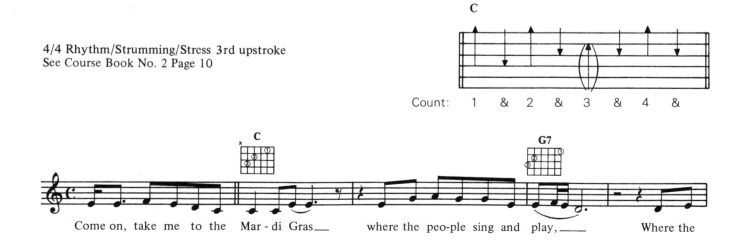

Count: 1 & 2 & 3 & 4 &

Come on, take me to the Mar - di Gras— where the peo-ple sing and play,— Where the

18

dancing is e-lite and there's mu-sic in the street both night and day. Hur-ry, take me to the

Mar-di-Gras,___ In the ci-ty of my dreams,___ You can le-gal-ize your laws, you can

wear your sum-mer clothes___ in the New Or-leans. And I will lay my bur-den down,___

Rest my head up-on that shore, And when I wear that star-ry crown, I won't be want-ing an-y

more.___ Take your bur-dens to the Mar-di Gras,___ Let the mu-sic wash your

soul,___ You can min-gle in the street, You can jin-gle in the beat of the jel-ly roll.___

Tum-ba, tum-ba, tum-ba, Mar-di Gras,___ Tum-ba, tum-ba, tum-ba day,___

Mm_____ Mm_____

Flowers Never Bend With The Rainfall Paul Simon

Verse 2

The mirror on my wall,
Casts an image dark and small,
But I'm not sure at all it's my reflection.

I am blinded by the light,
Of God and truth and right,
And I wander in the night without direction.

So I'll continue to continue to pretend,
My life will never end,
And flowers never bend with the rainfall.

Verse 3

No matter if you're born,
To play the King or pawn,
For the line is thinly drawn 'tween joy and sorrow.

So my fantasy,
Becomes reality,
And I must be what I must be and face tomorrow.

So I'll continue to pretend,
My life will never end,
And flowers never bend with the rainfall.

A Hazy Shade Of Winter Paul Simon

4/4 Rhythm/Strumming
See Course Book No. 2 Page 10

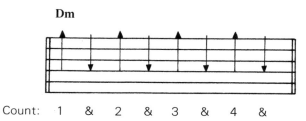

Count: 1 & 2 & 3 & 4 &

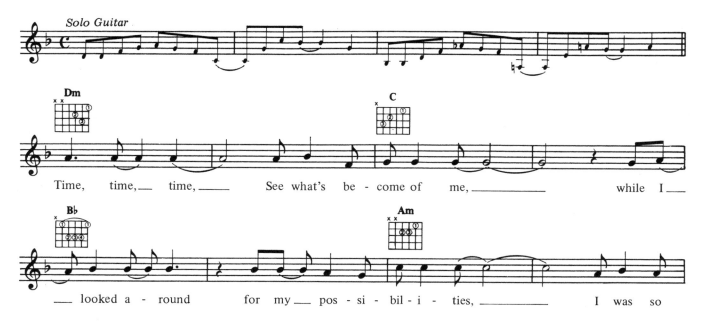

Solo Guitar

Time,   time,__ time,____   See what's be - come of   me,_____   while I __

__ looked a - round   for my __ pos - si - bil - i - ties, _____   I was so

At The Zoo Paul Simon

4/4 Rhythm/Arpeggio
See Course Book No. 2 Page 20

Count: 1 & 2 & 3 & 4 &

(Picked arpeggios)

Some-one told me, it's all hap-pen-ing at the zoo. _____ I do be-lieve _____ it, _____ I do be-lieve _____ it's true. _____ (Hum) _____

(Rhythm)

(Hum) _____ (Hum) _____ (Hum) _____

It's a light and tum-ble jour-ney, from the East-side to the park _____ Just a fine and fan-cy ram-ble to the zoo. _____

But you can take the cross-town bus, _____ if it's rain-in' or it's cold, _____ And the an-i-mals will love it, if _____ you do, _____ if you

(Picked arpeggios)

do. _____ Oo _____ Oo _____

Night Game   Paul Simon

4/4 Rhythm/Arpeggio
See Course Book No. 2 Page 20

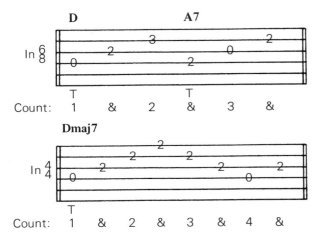

There were two men down, and the score was
tied in the bot - tom of the eighth when the pit - cher died. __
And they laid his spikes on the pit - cher's mound, and his
u - ni -form was torn, and his num - ber was left __ on the ground. Then the night turned
cold, cold - er than the moon. The stars were white as bones; the
sta-dium __ was old, old - er than the screams, old - er than the

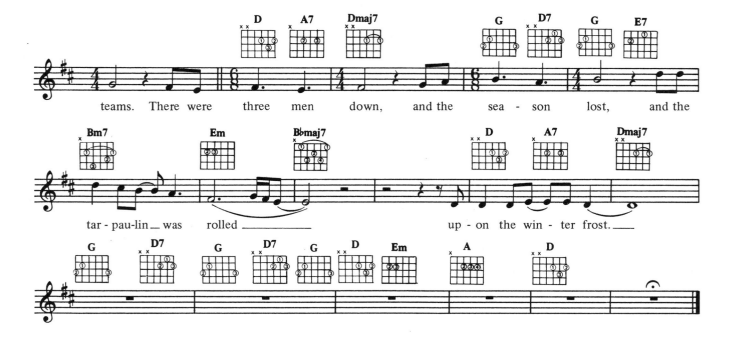

teams. There were three men down, and the sea-son lost, and the tar-pau-lin___ was rolled_____ up-on the win-ter frost.___

Duncan Paul Simon

4/4 Rhythm/Alternating Thumb
See Course Book No. 2 Page 25

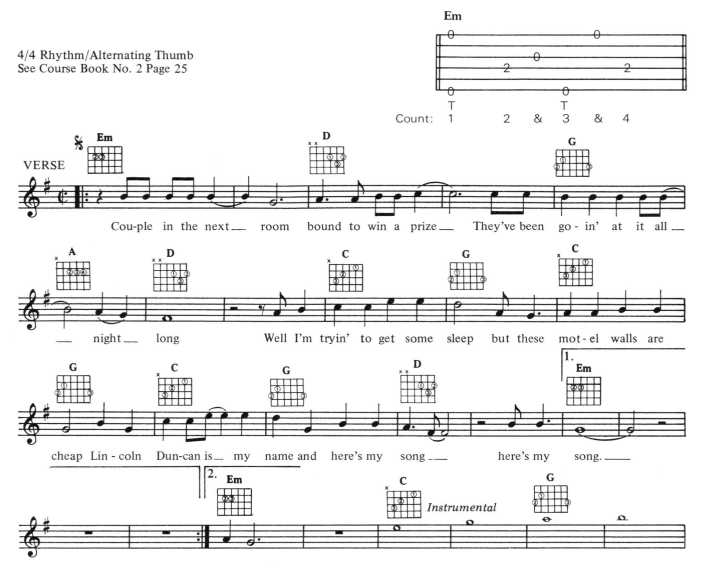

Count: 1 2 & 3 & 4

VERSE

Cou-ple in the next___ room bound to win a prize___ They've been go-in' at it all___ night___ long Well I'm tryin' to get some sleep but these mot-el walls are cheap Lin-coln Dun-can is___ my name and here's my song ___ here's my song.___

Instrumental

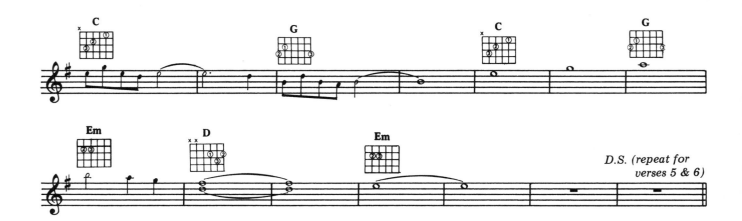

D.S. (repeat for verses 5 & 6)

Verse 2
My father was a fisherman, my mamma was a fisherman's friend,
And I was born in the boredom and the chowder,
So when I reached my prime,
I left my home in the Maritimes,
Headed down the turnpike for New England,
Sweet New England.
(Instrumental)

Verse 3 (On ⅅ.)
Holes in my confidence, holes in the knees of my jeans,
I's left without a penny in my pocket,
Oo hoo hoo wee, I's about destituted as a kid could be,
And I wished I wore a ring so I could hock it,
I'd like to hock it.

Verse 4
A young girl in a parking lot was preachin' to a crowd,
Singin' sacred songs and reading from the Bible,
Well I told her I was lost,
And she told me about the Pentecost,
And I seen that girl as the road to my survival.
(Instrumental)

Verse 5 (On ⅅ. 2nd time)
Just later on the very same night when I crept to her tent with a flashlight,
And my long years of innocence ended,
Well, she took me to the woods,
Sayin' "Here comes somethin' and it feels so good!"
And just like a dog I was befriended,
I was befriended.

Verse 6
Oh, oh, what a night, oh what a garden of delight,
Even now the sweet memory lingers,
I was playin' my guitar,
Lying underneath the stars,
Just thankin' the Lord for my fingers,
For my fingers.
(Instrumental and Fade)

Somewhere They Can't Find Me
Paul Simon

4/4/Rhythm/Bass-Strum/Swing
See Course Book No. 3 Page 11

Verse 2

Oh baby, you don't know what I've done
I've committed a crime, I've broken the law.
While you were sleeping; and just dreaming of me
I held up and robbed a liquor store.
Chorus

Verse 3

Oh my life seems unreal, my crime an illusion
A scene badly written in which I must play
And though it puts me up tight to leave you, —
I know it's not right to leave you.
When morning is just a few hours away.
Chorus

That Was Your Mother

Paul Simon

4/4 Rhythm/Strumming/Fast
See Course Book No. 3 Page 6

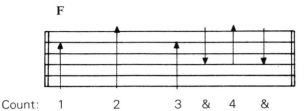

A long time a-go, yeah, __ be-fore __ you was born, dude, when I __ was still sin - gle and life was great, __ I held __ this job as __ a trav - el-ing sales-man __ that kept __ me mov-ing from state to state __

Well I'm stand-ing on the cor-ner of La - fa - yette, state of Lou-i - si - an - a, won-d'ring where a ci-ty boy could go _____ to get a lit - tle con-ver-sa - tion, __ drink a lit-tle red wine, catch a lit-tle bit of those Ca -jun girls __ danc-ing to Zy-de-co. __

1. 2.

3. A-long __ comes a

30

Verse 2
Along comes a young girl, she's pretty as a prayer book
Sweet as an apple on Christmas Day.
I said "Good gracious, can this be my luck?
If that's my prayer book, Lord let us pray."
Well, I'm standing on the corner of Lafayette, state of Louisiana
Wondering what a city boy could do.
To get her in a conversation, drink a little red wine,
Dance to the music of Clifton Chanier the King of Bayou.

Verse 3
Well that was your mother, that was your father,
Before you was born, dude when life was great.
You are the burden of my generation
I sure do love you. Let's get that straight.
Well, I'm standing on the corner of Lafayette,
Across the street from the public,
Heading down to the Lone Star Cafe
Maybe get a little conversation, drink a little red wine
Standing in the shadows on Clifton Chanier dancing the night away.

Was A Sunny Day Paul Simon

4/4 Rhythm/Syncopated arpeggio
See Course Book No. 3 Page 16

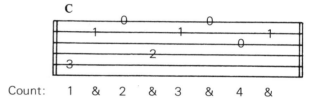

Verse 2
Her name was Lorelei,
She was the only girl
She called him "Speed-oo"
But his Christian name was Mister Earl
She called him "Speed-oo"
But his Christian name was Mister Earl.

Sparrow   Paul Simon

4/4 Rhythm/Arpeggio and alternating thumb mix
See Course Book No. 3 Page 25.

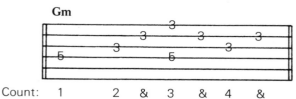

Count: 1   2 & 3 & 4 &

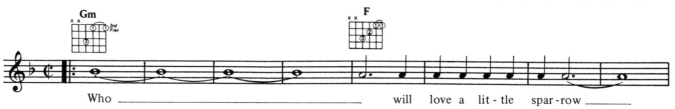

Who _____ will love a lit - tle spar-row _____

who's trav - elled far _____ and cries for rest? _____

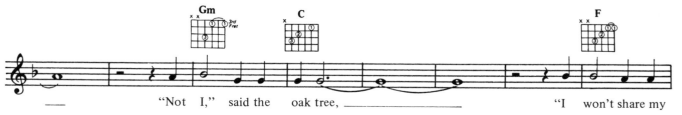

—— "Not I," said the oak tree, _____ "I won't share my

branch-es with no spar-row's nest, _____ And my blank-et of leaves won't warm her cold

breast." _____

Verse 2
Who will love a little sparrow,
And who will speak a kindly word?
"Not I,"said the swan,
"The entire idea is utterly absurd,
I'd be laughed at and scorned if the other swans heard."

Verse 3
Who will take pity in his heart,
And who will feed a starving sparrow?
"Not I,"said the golden wheat,
"I would if I could but I cannot I know,
I need all my grain to prosper and grow."

Verse 4
Who will love a little sparrow?
Will no one write her eulogy?
"I will,"said the earth,
"For all I've created returns unto me,
From dust were ye made and dust ye shall be."

The Fifty-Ninth Street Bridge Song
(Feelin' Groovy) Paul Simon

4/4 Rhythm/Bass-Strum/Swing
See Course Book No. 3 Page 11

34

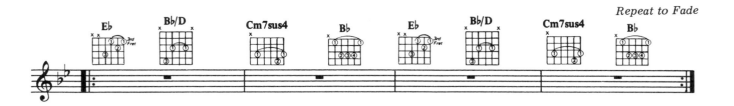

Repeat to Fade

El Condor Pasa (If I Could) J. Milchberg, D. Robles & Paul Simon

4/4 Rhythm/Syncopated Arpeggio
See Course Book No. 3 Page 16

Think of as two arpeggios joined together per bar.

I'd rath-er be a spar-row than a snail. Yes I would. If I could, I sure-ly

would.— Hm — I'd rath-er be a ham-mer than a nail. Yes I would. If I on-ly

could, — I sure-ly would.— Hm — A-way, I'd rath-er sail a-way — Like a

swan that's here and gone. A man gets tied up to the ground, He gives the world its sad-dest

sound, its sad-dest sound. — I'd rath-er be a for-est than a

street. Yes I would. If I could,— I sure-ly would.— I'd rath-er feel the earth be-neath my

feet. Yes I would. If I on-ly could, — I sure-ly would.—

Still Crazy After All These Years   Paul Simon

3/4 Rhythm/Arpeggio/Slight Swing
See Course Book No. 3 Page 13

Count: 1   2   &   3   &

I met my old lov-er on the street last night; she seemed so glad to

see me, I just smiled. And we talked a-bout some old times and we

drank our-selves some beers. Still cra-zy af-ter all these years; oh, still cra-zy af-ter

all these years. I'm not the years.

Four in the morn-ing; crapped out, yawn-ing; long-ing my life a-way.

I'll nev-er wor-ry; why should I? It's all gon-na fade.

Now I sit by my win-dow and I watch the cars;

I fear I'll do some dam-age one fine day. But I would not be con-vic-ted by a ju-ry of my peers.__ Still cra-zy__ af-ter all __ these__ years; oh, still cra-zy, ___ still cra-zy. still cra-zy__ af-ter all __ these__ years.

Verse 2
I'm not the kind of man who tends to socialize
I seem to lean on old familiar ways
And I ain't no fool for love songs
That whisper in my ears
Still crazy after all these years . . . .

A Poem On The Underground Wall Paul Simon

4/4 Rhythm/Alternating thumb
See Course Book No. 3 Page 23

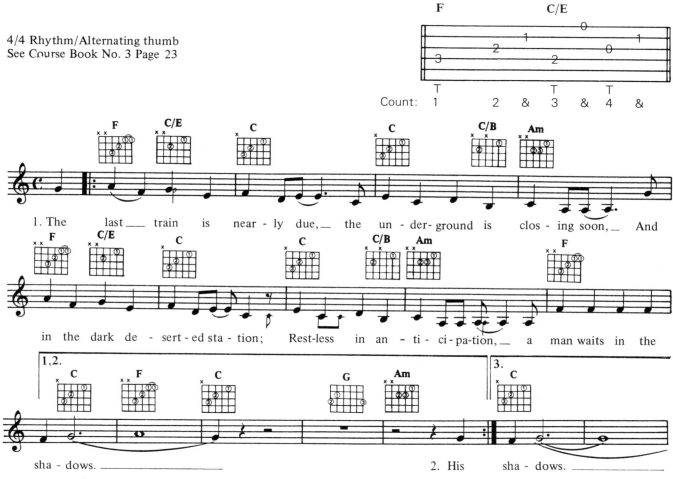

1. The last __ train is near-ly due,__ the un-der-ground is clos-ing soon,__ And in the dark de-sert-ed sta-tion; Rest-less in an-ti-ci-pa-tion,__ a man waits in the

sha - dows. _____ 2. His sha - dows. _____

Verse 2
His restless eyes leap and scratch,
At all that they can touch or catch,
And hidden deep within his pocket,
Safe within his silent socket,
He holds his coloured crayon.

Verse 3
Now from the tunnel's stony womb,
The carriage rides to meet the groom,
And opens wide and welcome doors,
But he hesitates, then withdraws,
Deeper in the shadows.

Verse 5
And his heart is laughing, screaming, pounding,
The poem across the tracks rebounding,
Shadowed by the exit light,
His legs take their ascending flight,
To seek the breast of darkness and be suckled by the night.

We've Got A Groovy Thing Goin' Paul Simon

4/4 Rhythm/Strumming/Stress 1st beat and 1st upstroke
See Course Book No. 4 Page 10

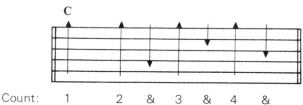

Count: 1   2 & 3 & 4 &

Verse 2
I never done you no wrong.
I never hit you when you're down.
I always gave you good lovin'.
I never ran around
I never ran around.
Oh baby, baby *etc.*

Verse 3
There's something you ought to know
If you're fixin' to go,
I can't make it without you
No, no, no, no, no, no, no —
No, no, no, no, no, no, no, no.
Oh baby *etc.*

Loves Me Like A Rock   Paul Simon

4/4 Rhythm/Strumming/Swing/Damp Strokes
See Course Book No. 4 Page 11

1. When I was a lit-tle boy,— (When I — was just a boy.) and the dev-il would call my

name, (When I — was just a boy.) I'd say, "Now who do,— who do you think you're fool-

ing?" (When I — was just a boy.) I'm a con-se-crat-ed boy.(When I — was just a boy.) I'm a sing-er in the

Sun-day choir,—   Oh,— my ma-ma loves me, she loves — me.   She get down on her knees and hug

— me like she loves me like a rock.   She rock me like a rock of ag - es and loves—

— me. —   She love me, love me, love me, love me.—   2. When I was grown to be a

man, (Grown — to be a man.) and the de-vil would call my name, (Grown — to be a man.) I'd say, "Now

who do,— who do you think you're fool - ing?" (Grown — to be a man.) I'm a con-sum-mat-ed

man, (Grown to be a man.) I can snatch a lit-tle pu - ri-ty, My ma-ma loves me, she loves

me. She get down on her knees and hug me like she loves me like a rock.

She rocks me like the rock of a - ges and loves me. She love me, love me, love me,

love me. 3. And if I was the Pres - i - dent, (Was the Pres-i - dent.) the min-ute the Con - gress call my

name. (Was the Pres - i - dent.) I say, "Now who do, who do you think you're fool -

(Who do you think you're fool - ing?")
ing?" I've got the Pres - i - den-tial Seal, (Was the Pres - i -

dent.) I'm up on the Pres - i - den-tial Po - di - um. My ma - ma loves me, she loves

me. She get down on her knees and hug me like she loves me like a rock.

She rocks me like the rock of a - ges and loves me. She love me, love me, love me,

Repeat to Fade

(Love me like a rock.) (Love me like a
love me. She love me, love me, love me, love me.

Keep The Customer Satisfied Paul Simon

4/4 Rhythm/Slap style/Swing
See Course Book No. 4 Page 11

Gee but it's great to be back home, Home is where I want to be.

___ I've been on the road so long my friend, And if you came a- long I know you couldn't dis-a - gree..

___ It's the same old sto-ry ___ (Yeah) Ev-'ry-where I go ___ I get slan-dered,

Li - belled, ___ I hear words ___ I nev - er heard in the Bi - ble. ___ And I'm one step a- head of the

shoe shine, Two steps a-way from the county line, Just trying to keep my cus-tom-ers sat -is-fied, Sat - is -

1. fied. ___ **2.** fied. ___ Woh ___ Woh ___ Woh ___

Woh ___ But it's the same old sto-ry ___

___ Ev-'ry-where I go, ___ I get slan-dered, Li - belled, ___ I hear words ___

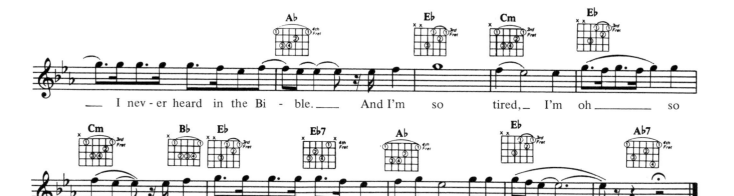

_ I nev - er heard in the Bi - ble. And I'm so tired,_ I'm oh __ so

tired,__ But I'm trying to keep my cus-tom-ers sat - is -fied, Sat-is - fied. ____

Verse 2

Deputy Sheriff said to me,
Tell me what you come here for, boy,
You better get your bags and flee,
You're in trouble boy, and now you're heading into more,
It's the same old story (yeah).

Ev'rywhere I go I get slandered,
Libelled,
I hear words I never heard in the Bible,
And I'm one step ahead of the shoe shine,
Two steps away from the county line,
Just trying to keep my customers satisfied,
Satisfied.

Woh, woh, woh, woh.

But it's the same old story,
Ev'rywhere I go,
I get slandered,
Libelled,
I hear words I never heard in the Bible,
And I'm so tired,
I'm oh so tired,
But I'm trying to keep my customers satisfied,
Satisfied.

Fifty Ways To Leave Your Lover Paul Simon

4/4 Rhythm/Syncopated arpeggio and thumb mix
See Course Book No. 4 Page 15

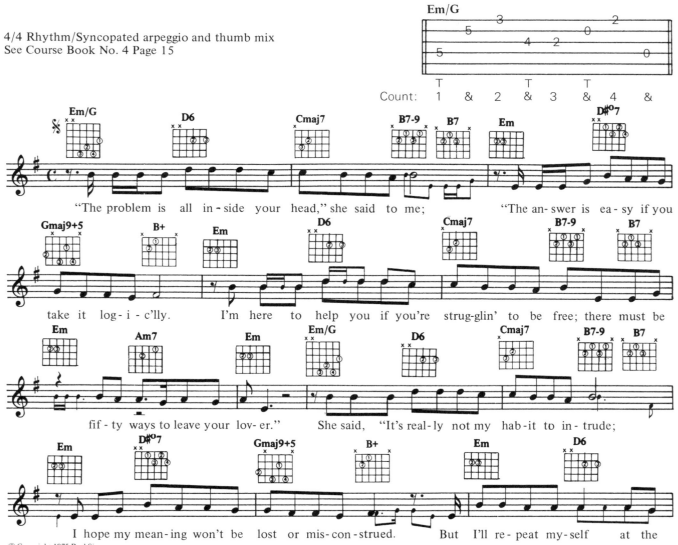

"The problem is all in -side your head," she said to me; "The an- swer is ea- sy if you

take it log- i - c'lly. I'm here to help you if you're strug-glin' to be free; there must be

fif - ty ways to leave your lov- er." She said, "It's real-ly not my hab-it to in- trude;

I hope my mean-ing won't be lost or mis-con-strued. But I'll re-peat my-self at the

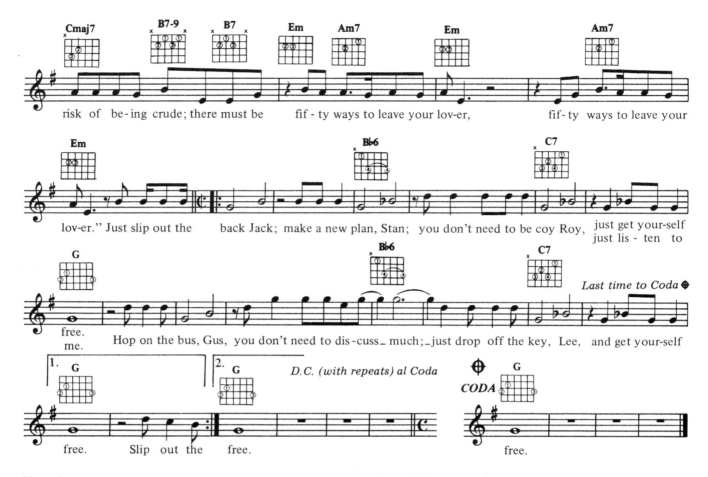

risk of be-ing crude; there must be fif-ty ways to leave your lov-er, fif-ty ways to leave your

lov-er." Just slip out the back Jack; make a new plan, Stan; you don't need to be coy Roy, just get your-self / just lis-ten to

free. / me. Hop on the bus, Gus, you don't need to dis-cuss_ much;_just drop off the key, Lee, and get your-self

Last time to Coda

1. G free. Slip out the free.
2. G *D.C. (with repeats) al Coda*
CODA G free.

Verse 2
She said "It grieves me now to see you in such pain;
I wish there was somethin' I could do to make you smile again,
I said "I appreciate that, and could you please explain,
About the Fifty Ways?"

She said "Why don't we both just sleep on it tonight,
I'm sure in the morning you'll begin to see the light."
And then she kissed me and I realised
She probably was right;
There must be Fifty Ways To Leave Your Lover,
Fifty Ways To Leave Your Lover.

Bookends Paul Simon

3/8 Rhythm/Arpeggio and embellishments with 6th's
See Course Book No. 4 Pages 16-22 and Page 26

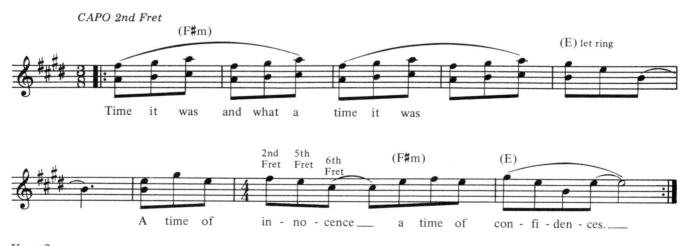

Time it was and what a time it was

A time of in-no-cence_ a time of con-fi-den-ces._

Verse 2
Long ago it must be
I have a photograph

Preserve your memories
They're all that's left you.

Scarborough Fair/Canticle Paul Simon & Art Garfunkel

3/4 Rhythm/Arpeggio and embellishments
See Course Book No. 4 Pages 16-22

CAPO 2nd Fret

Introduction

Verses

(C shape)

Repeat for Verses 2 to 5

Verses

Are   you   go-ing ___ to   Scar-bor-ough Fair _____   Pars-ley, sage, rose-ma-ry and

thyme _____   Re - mem - ber   me   to   one who lives   there _____

She   once   was   a   true love   of   mine _____

Last x rall.

Verse 2
Tell her to make a cambric shirt,
Parsley, sage, rosemary and thyme,
Without no seams nor needle work,
Then she'll be a true love of mine.

On the side of a hill in the deep forest green,
Tracing of sparrow on snowcrested brown.
Blankets and bedclothes the child of the mountain,
Sleeps unaware of the clarion call.

Verse 3
Tell her to find me an acre of land,
Parsley, sage, rosemary and thyme,
Between the salt water and the sea strands,
Then she'll be a true love of mine.

On the side of a hill a sprinkling of leaves,
Washes the grave with silvery tears.
A soldier cleans and polishes a gun,
Sleeps unaware of the clarion call.

Verse 4
Tell her to reap it with a sickle of leather,
Parsley, sage, rosemary and thyme,
And gather it all in a bunch of heather,
Then she'll be a true love of mine.

War bellows blazing in scarlet battalions,
Generals order their soldiers to kill,
And to fight for a cause they've long ago forgotten.

Verse 5
Are you going to Scarborough Fair,
Parsley, sage, rosemary and thyme,
Remember me to one who lives there,
She once was a true love of mine.

You Can Call Me Al Paul Simon

4/4 Rhythm/Syncopated Strumming and Fills
See Course Book No. 4 Pages 16-22 and Page 26

Rhythm pattern throughout Chorus and Introduction

4 bar phrase repeated 4 times per Verse.

A man walks down the street, he says, "Why am I soft in the mid-dle now? Why am I soft in the middle, the

rest of my life is so hard. I need a pho-to op-por-tu-ni-ty, I want a shot at re-demp-tion.

Don't want to end up a car-toon in a car-toon grave-yard." Bone dig-ger, bone dig-ger,

dogs in the moon-light far a-way in my well-lit door. Mis-ter beer bel-ly, beer bel-ly,

get these mutts a-way from me. I don't find this stuff a-mus-ing an-y-more.

If you'll be my bo-dy-guard I can be your long lost pal.

To Coda ⊕

C B♭ F C F |1. F C B♭ F C F

I can call you Bet-ty   and Bet-ty, when you call me, you can call me Al.

|2. F C B♭ F C F

Tacet   *D.C. al Coda*

call   me   Al ____   Call   me   Al.

⊕ *CODA*

F C B♭ F C F C F *Rhythm as Verses* G F C

call   me   Al. ___   Call   me.   Na _ na   na na   na _ na   na na.

F C F F C Gm F

Na _ na   na na   Na _ na na na na.   Hm,   hm,   hm hm.

|1. Gm C |2. Gm C F

Bass solo

As Chorus

F C B♭ F C F C B♭ F C

Repeat and Fade

F C B♭ F C F F C B♭ F C F

If you'll be my bo-dy-guard
I can call you Bet-ty. ___

Verse 2
A man walks down the street
He says why am I short of attention
Got a short little span of attention
And oh my nights are so long
Where's my wife and family
What if I die here
Who'll be my role-model
Now that my role-model is
Gone Gone
He ducked back down the alley
With some roly-poly little bat-faced girl
All along along
There were incidents and accidents
There were hints and allegations.
Chorus

Verse 3
A man walks down the street
It's a street in a strange world
Maybe it's the Third World
Maybe it's his first time around
He doesn't speak the language
He holds no currency
He is a foreign man
He is surrounded by the sound
The sound
Cattle in the marketplace
Scatterlings and orphanages
He looks around, around
He sees angels in the architecture
Spinning in infinity
He says Amen! and Hallelujah!
Chorus

For Emily, Whenever I May Find Her Paul Simon

4/4 Rhythm/Arpeggios and embelishments
See Course Book No. 4 Pages 16-22

What a dream___ I had   Pressed in or - gan - dy,   Clothed in

crin-o - line ___   of smo- key bur-gun - dy   Soft - er than the   rain. ___

___(girl)___   oh,   I ___   love ___   you. ___

Verse 2
I wandered empty streets down past the shop displays.
I heard cathedral bells tripping down the alley ways.
As I walked on.

Verse 3
And when you ran to me your cheeks flushed with the night,
We walked on frosted fields of juniper and lamplight,
I held your hand.

Verse 4
And when I awoke and felt you warm and near,
I kissed your honey hair with my grateful tears.
Oh I love you, girl,
Oh, I love you.

9/91(12447)